NAT FANTASTIC

AND THE
BRAVE KNIGHTS
OF OLD

ORCHARD BOOKS
338 Euston Road, London NW1 3BH
Orchard Books Australia
Level 17/207, Kent Street, Sydney, NSW 2000

First published by Orchard Books in 2010

Text © Giles Andreae 2010
Illustrations © Katharine McEwen 2010
The rights of Giles Andreae to be identified as the author
and of Katharine McEwen to be identified as the illustrator
of this Work have been asserted by them in accordance
with the Copyright, Designs and Patents Act, 1988.

A CIP catalogue record of this book
is available from the British Library.

ISBN: 978 1 40830 517 1
10 9 8 7 6 5 4 3 2 1

Printed in China

Orchard Books is a division of Hachette Children's Books,
an Hachette UK company.
www.hachette.co.uk

NAT FANTASTIC

AND THE
BRAVE KNIGHTS
OF OLD

Giles Andreae

Katharine McEwen

ORCHARD BOOKS

This is Nat. He is playing a game and
hoping his mummy will make him sausages,
baked beans, egg and chips for tea.
This is his favourite. Especially the sausages.

"I'll just go and turn on the cooker," said his mummy.
"Now, be a good boy and start putting your knights away."

As soon as his mummy went into the kitchen,

Nat's nose began to tingle.

The tingle grew tinglier and tinglier until . . .

"AAACHOOOO!"

Nat sneezed an almighty sneeze.

FLASH!

BANG!

WHIZZ!

KABOOM!

NAT FANTASTIC'S IN THE ROOM!

And he was.

That sneeze had changed Nat into a miniature superhero!

Suddenly Nat felt himself
whizzing through the air
at a million miles an hour.

Then

BUMP!

he landed right on top of

an enormous horse!

And not only that . . .
Nat found that he was wearing an
amazing silver suit of armour.

Then a man passed him a long lance.
"Good luck, brave knight!" he said.
Nat's horse began galloping
across a field right
towards another knight;
a knight dressed entirely
in black armour.

The knight was much bigger
than Nat and he looked
very scary indeed, but
Nat lowered his lance and

SPROING!

the knight went flying out of his saddle

and landed with a

PLOP!

in

the

lake.

"You're amazing, Nat Fantastic!" swooned a
damsel who was running towards him.
"The Black Knight has held
me captive until the day that
he was defeated in a duel.
You have freed me!"

And she gave Nat a huge
kiss on the cheek, which
Nat really quite liked.

Suddenly Nat felt his nose begin to tingle again.

It got tinglier and tinglier until . . .

"AAA...

...CHOOO!"

Nat sneezed an
almighty sneeze,
and he was
back at home.

At that very moment
Nat's mummy called out.
"Tea's ready, darling.
Come and sit down."

After a little while Nat's mummy said,
"Oh good, the washing machine's finished.
Do you mind if I hang out the laundry?

I'll be back in just a minute."

Immediately Nat's nose began
to tingle. The tingle grew
tinglier and tinglier until . . .

Nat sneezed an almighty sneeze.

"AAACHOOOO!"

FLASH!

BANG!

WHIZZ!

KABOOM!

NAT FANTASTIC'S
IN THE ROOM!

Suddenly Nat felt himself whizzing through
the air at a million miles an hour until . . .

...SPLOSH!

he landed right in the moat of a knights' castle! Nat stood up and found he was wearing his amazing suit of armour again – and this time he had a giant sword in one hand and a shield in the other.

"Come on!" shouted a man beside him. "The baddies have captured our castle. We must get it back and save our friends inside!"

Soon he and the other knights had charged through the gates of the castle and tied up the baddies.

"Nat Fantastic's a hero!"

"We must make him a
special Knight of Honour!"
And they gave him a gleaming silver shield.
Nat was very pleased with this indeed.
Suddenly Nat felt his nose begin to tingle again.
It got tinglier and tinglier until . . .

"AAACHOOOO!"

Nat sneezed an almighty sneeze and he was back in his kitchen at home. At that moment Nat's mummy walked back into the room. "There we go," she said. "All done. Have you seen my glasses anywhere, darling?"

"I think they're in my bedroom," said Nat. "You left them there when you were reading to me last night."

So Nat's mummy went upstairs to find them.

Nat's nose began to tingle. The tingle grew tinglier and tinglier until . . .

"AAACHOOOO!"

Nat sneezed an almighty sneeze.

FLASH!

BANG!

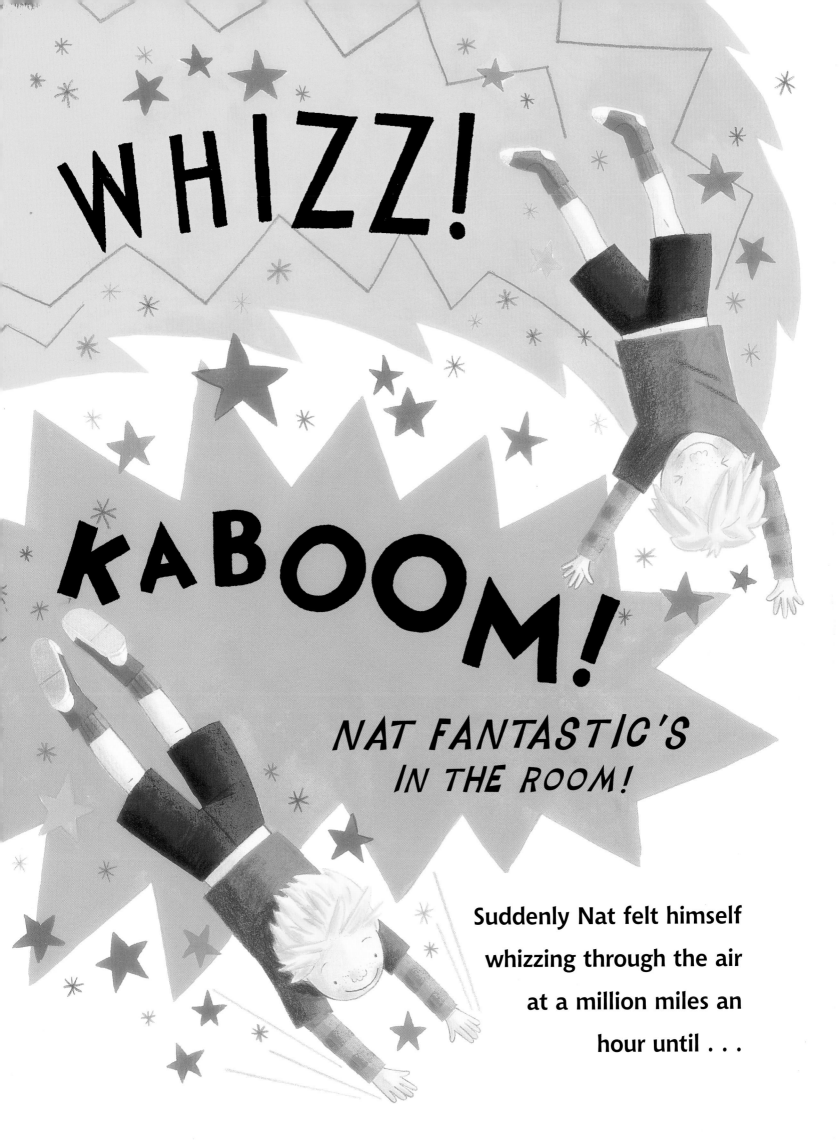

WHIZZ!

KABOOM!

NAT FANTASTIC'S
IN THE ROOM!

Suddenly Nat felt himself
whizzing through the air
at a million miles an
hour until . . .

. . . BOING!

he landed (in his amazing silver suit of armour again) right on top of a large purple cushion that was on the seat of an ENORMOUS throne.

The throne was in the middle of a very long table where
there were lots of other knights enjoying the biggest feast
that Nat Fantastic had ever seen! It looked delicious.

And right in front of Nat was a
HUGE plate full of sausages!

"And now," said a man, "it is time to
honour the bravest knight of all."

He lifted up a big gold crown covered with jewels
and placed it on Nat's head.

"Nat Fantastic," he said, "You are the boldest knight
amongst us and now we crown you as our king!"

Everybody began to clap and cheer.

Suddenly Nat felt his nose begin to tingle again.

It got tinglier and tinglier until . . .

"AAACHOOOO!"

Nat sneezed an almighty sneeze and

he was back in his kitchen at home.

At that very moment Nat's mummy
walked back into the room.
"That's better," she said,
putting on her glasses.
"Now, have you
finished your egg?"

"No, mummy," said Nat.
"But I've eaten a lot of
sausages. Can I get down
and play please?"

"OK," said his mummy.
"And be a good boy now."

So Nat went into the garden.

But guess what . . .

Just as Nat was beginning to
play with his favourite car . . .

he felt his nose begin to tingle!

Oh no, Nat! Not now . . .

Not while you're right there
in the garden!

Luckily, Nat knew what was coming so he took out a handkerchief and blew his nose.

"That's better," he thought.
. . . But it wasn't!

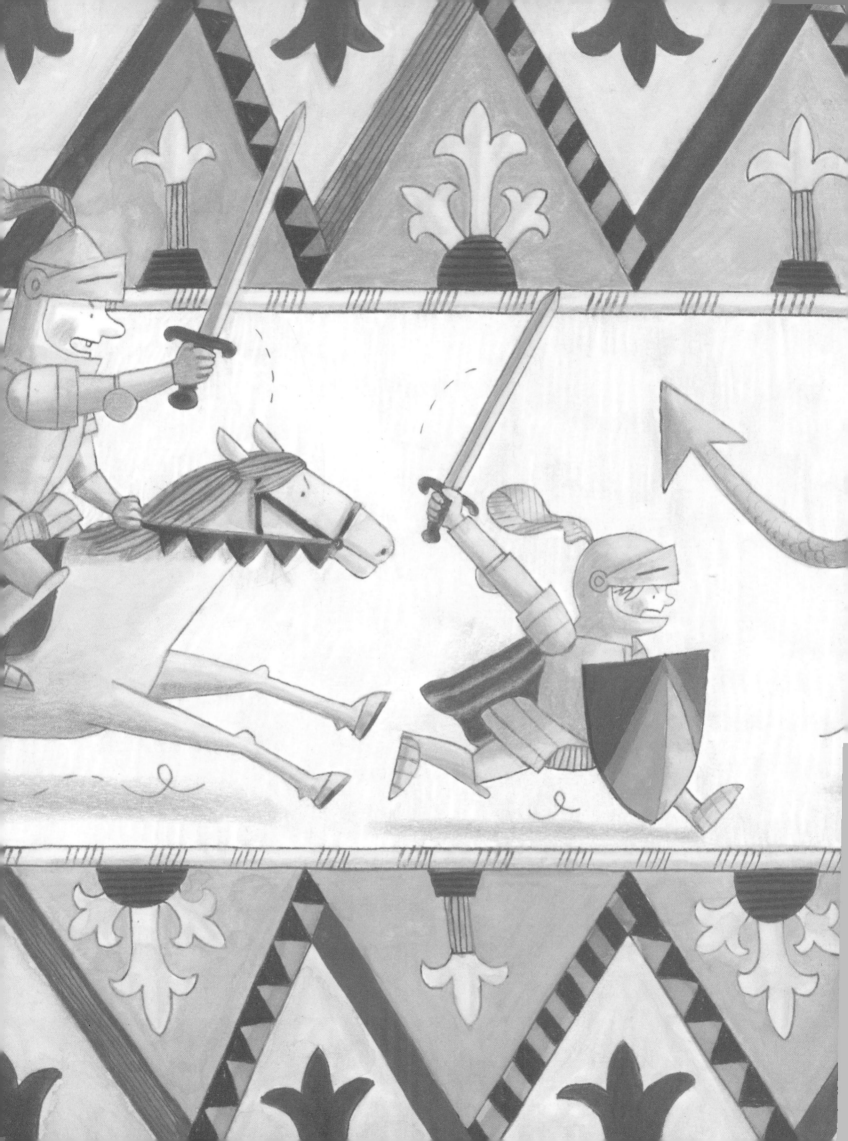